Punctuation ★ Tales ★

sentence stoppers

Little Red Hen Bakes a Cake

by Liza Charlesworth
illustrated by Jim Paillot

SCHOLASTIC INC.

New York • Toronto • London • Auckland • Sydney
Mexico City • New Delhi • Hong Kong • Buenos Aires

Designed by Grafica, Inc.
ISBN-13: 978-0-545-01434-2 • ISBN-10: 0-545-01434-4
Copyright © 2007 by Lefty's Editorial Services.
All rights reserved. Printed in the U.S.A.

First printing, October 2007

12 11 10 9 8 7 6 5 4 3 2 1   7 8 9 10 11 12/0

Sentence Stopper Fact:
All sentences end with one of three sentence stoppers: a period (.), a question mark (?), or an exclamation point (!). Without one of these sentence stoppers in place, a sentence just isn't a sentence.

Once upon a time, there lived a cool chicken named Little Red Hen.

Little Red Hen had a lot of hobbies. She loved to skateboard. She loved to paint. But more than anything else in the world, she loved to bake!

One day, Little Red Hen decided to bake a cake. But what kind should she make? She thought and thought. Then she found a recipe for triple-chocolate layer cake with banana-cream filling and blueberry-jellybean frosting. It sounded delicious! "This is the cake that I will bake," she said.

Sentence Stopper Fact:
Most sentences are *declarative sentences*. Declarative sentences make a statement and end with a period. Look at the speech balloons on these two pages. Each contains a declarative sentence.

Cluck, cluck, cluck! Little Red Hen ran off to the grocery store. There, she loaded up a cart with everything she needed to bake the cake.

When she got back home, Little Red Hen unpacked her grocery bags. There were so many ingredients! Baking this cake was going to be very hard work.

Then Little Red Hen got a great idea! She went to see her friends Dog, Duck, and Cat. Would they help her bake the cake?

To her amazement, all three friends told her no. Dog had to read a comic book. Duck had to hang up some wet socks. And Cat absolutely, positively had to take a very long nap.

Sentence Stopper Fact:
Exclamatory sentences express strong feelings and end with an exclamation point. Look at the speech balloons on these two pages. Each contains an exclamatory sentence.

Little Red Hen was so disappointed. "Dear me!" she said excitedly. "I will just have to bake the cake all by myself!"

So she did. Little Red Hen measured and sifted and mixed. She stirred and spiced and poured. She whipped and baked and finally frosted.

At last, the cake was ready. Little Red Hen proudly placed it on the table. *Cluck, cluck, cluck!* The kitchen was a disaster, but the cake looked divine. And it smelled delicious!

The sweet smell of cake drifted out the window and into the backyard. Dog closed his comic book. Duck dropped his socks. Cat woke up from her nap. What was that wonderful scent? They all raced into the kitchen!

Sentence Stopper Fact:
Imperative sentences give an order or ask for something. They usually end with a period, but sometimes end with an exclamation point. Look at the speech balloons on these two pages. Each contains an imperative sentence.

When Dog, Duck, and Cat saw the cake, they each demanded a piece. Should Little Red Hen share her cake with them? It was true that they were her friends. But it was also true that they hadn't helped one tiny bit. Little Red Hen thought and thought. Then she finally said . . .

Sentence Stopper Fact:
As you can see from this tale, all sentences end with a period, a question mark, or an exclamation point. Now read the story again and pay careful attention to how each of them is used. Are you ready? Have fun!

"Okay, you can each have a piece. But you guys have to wash ALL of those dishes when you are done."

Dog, Duck, and Cat eagerly agreed. Then the four friends sat down to eat the cake. And it was absolutely, positively scrumptious!

Rule Round-Up

THE BIG IDEA: All sentences end with one of three sentence stoppers: a period, a question mark, or an exclamation point.

This is a period:	This is a question mark:	This is an exclamation point:
.	?	!

There are four different kinds of sentences.

1. Declarative sentences make a statement and end with a period. Most sentences are declarative sentences.

   EXAMPLE: *I am going to bake a scrumptious cake.*

2. Interrogative sentences ask a question and end with a question mark.

   EXAMPLE: *Who will help me bake my cake?*

3. Exclamatory sentences express strong emotion and end with an exclamation point.

   EXAMPLE: *I will just have to bake the cake all by myself!*

4. Imperative sentences give an order or ask for something. They usually end with a period, but sometimes end with an exclamation point.

   EXAMPLE 1: *Please give me cake.*

   EXAMPLE 2: *Don't do that!*

TERRIFIC TIP!

If you are not sure what type of punctuation to use at the end of your sentence, try this: Pretend you're an actor and read the sentence aloud extra dramatically.

1. Does it sound like you're making a regular statement? Use a period.

2. Does it sound like you're asking a question? Use a question mark.

3. Does it sound like you're excited or shouting? Use an exclamation point.

4. Does it sound like you're giving an order? Use either a period or an exclamation point.

Punctuation Bingo

Which of these nine sentences end with the correct sentence stopper? Mark them with buttons or pennies. Get three in a row and you win! (Bingo can be vertical, horizontal, or diagonal.)

1. Do you know the story called "The Little Red Hen!"	**2.** Dog really liked to read comic books about superheroes?	**3.** Close the door.
4. Would you like to try Little Red Hen's cake.	**5.** Cat took a very long nap every afternoon.	**6.** Little Red Hen bought ten enormous bags of groceries!
7. Would you like to iron your socks?	**8.** I think I will go to sleep,	**9.** Don't do that?

EXTRA! Write a mini-play starring Little Red Hen, Dog, Duck, and Cat. In it, try to use each sentence stopper at least three times.

Answers: The sentences that use the correct sentence stoppers are 3, 5, 6, and 7. Bingo is 3, 5, and 7.